Please, Nana

Who is God?

Written by Margaret Wieland

Illustrated by Caleb Salisbury

Author's note

This is a book to be *read to* (with) children, not just given to them.

In recent years I have been blessed to have the company of a little one who has grown up asking questions. Some I could answer easily—others took a bit more thought—and still others caused me to find simpler ways of explaining some of the most profound truths, which always come back to the biggest issue of them all—God and the way His Word intersects with our lives and all of reality. Whilst I think (like all grandparents, I suppose) that she is a special child, I know that her questions are not unique. The questions—and their answers—are told in simple language, with added explanations for the reader where they might be useful.

I can think of no better way for a little child to learn the realities of the universe than on the lap of a loving adult. It is my prayer that adults and children will treasure the time shared together, as we did, while laying a solid biblical foundation in young minds.

Published and distributed by

CREATION
BOOK PUBLISHERS

www.creationbookpublishers.com

Author's Dedication

To my darling 'granddaughter' Mary-Beth: you have so enriched my life that it would be wrong not to share some of our experiences together with others.

www.pleasenana.com

For information on creation/evolution issues and materials for all ages, visit:

CREATION.com

ISBN: 9781921643187

First printing 2010

Hi—I'm Bilby, a small, cute and cuddly looking animal that lives in Australia. I'm Nana's friend, and I can be yours too—look for me on every double-page spread.

Let me tell you about the 'Nana Notes'.
On some pages where you see a tiny Nana Head and small number next to a word, like this, (look it up in the back of the book!) it means Nana has written notes to help explain things a bit more.

[1] Bilby

[1] A bilby is a small cute Australian animal (for more information see p.24).

About the Author:

Margaret Wieland is the eldest of seven children, a Christian for well over 50 years, a mother, grandmother and great grandmother who (though widely traveled) has lived in Australia all her life. She is fond of telling anyone who listens that "these later years are the best time of life, particularly if you can share that life with young children. They make you look at familiar things with fresh eyes and bring a newness of life to old beliefs. There are no greater treasures we can leave a child (related or not) than our unconditional love, our unhurried time, a love for God and His Word, and as many shared experiences as possible. It's the closest thing to the 'Fountain of Youth' you will ever find."

About the Illustrator:

Caleb Salisbury is a professional illustrator with an extensive background in game development and graphic design. He grew up in Africa and now lives in Brisbane (Australia), where he enjoys creating entertaining stories featuring whimsical characters and visually rich environments for all ages. He currently works for *Creation Ministries International*.

He says he also drinks far too much coffee.

Acknowledgment

Before I started on this venture, I believed that writing books for children would be less difficult than writing for adults. "Iron sharpens iron" indeed (Proverbs 27:17) and this book is as useful as it was meant to be because a number of gifted, mature Christians made invaluable contributions. It is hard to name them all; some simply gave encouragement, others pointed out where either words or drawings needed adjustment in order to remain true to the Word of God, while the editorial skills of quite a few were vital. To them, and to those who had already written much on this subject and whose work I have unashamedly utilized—my heartfelt thanks. And it goes without saying, perhaps, that without Caleb's magnificent drawings, these simple words would not have sprung so profoundly to life.

www.pleasenana.com

We snuggled up real close in church,
Like two peas in a pod,
When suddenly the question came:
"Please, Nana, who is God?"

I turned to quietly tell her, "Hush."
I couldn't answer then.
But, "Wait," I thought, "Best do it now;
She might not ask again."

We walked outside to where the world
Was bathed in warm sunlight;
I prayed to God, "Oh, help me, please—
I've got to get this right."

In silence first we strolled along
As usual, hand in hand.
And slowly then my thoughts took shape;
She just might understand.

"It's really hard explaining God—"
(Though I would surely try)
"Unless we find out what He did:
The when, the how, the why."

"There was a time when nothing was—
No land, no sea or sky,
No birds or plants or animals,
And not one butterfly." ²

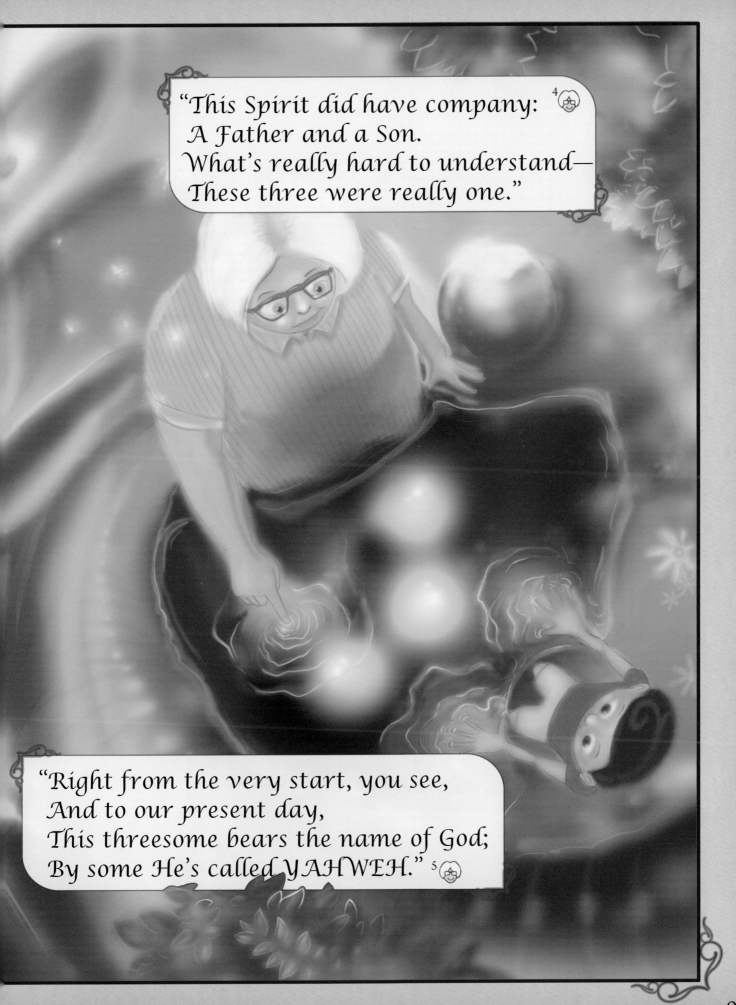

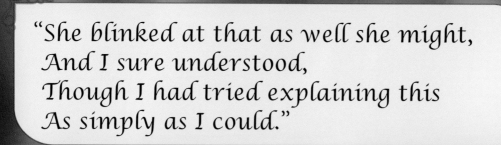

"She blinked at that as well she might,
And I sure understood,
Though I had tried explaining this
As simply as I could."

"There was no turning back from here,
This story should be told;
So, big deep breath and on I went,
This myst'ry to unfold."

"God knew how special it would be
To share His company;
He set about to find a way
Of making you and me." [6]

"First came the earth all big and round,
And sea without a border;
A light so bright it split the dark
To bring about some order."

"And then above this watery world,
God made what we call sky;
It was a place where clouds would float
And where the birds would fly."

"Tall mountains, hills and valleys, too,
Began to split the sea;
Rivers flowed from lake to shore—
God traced them carefully."

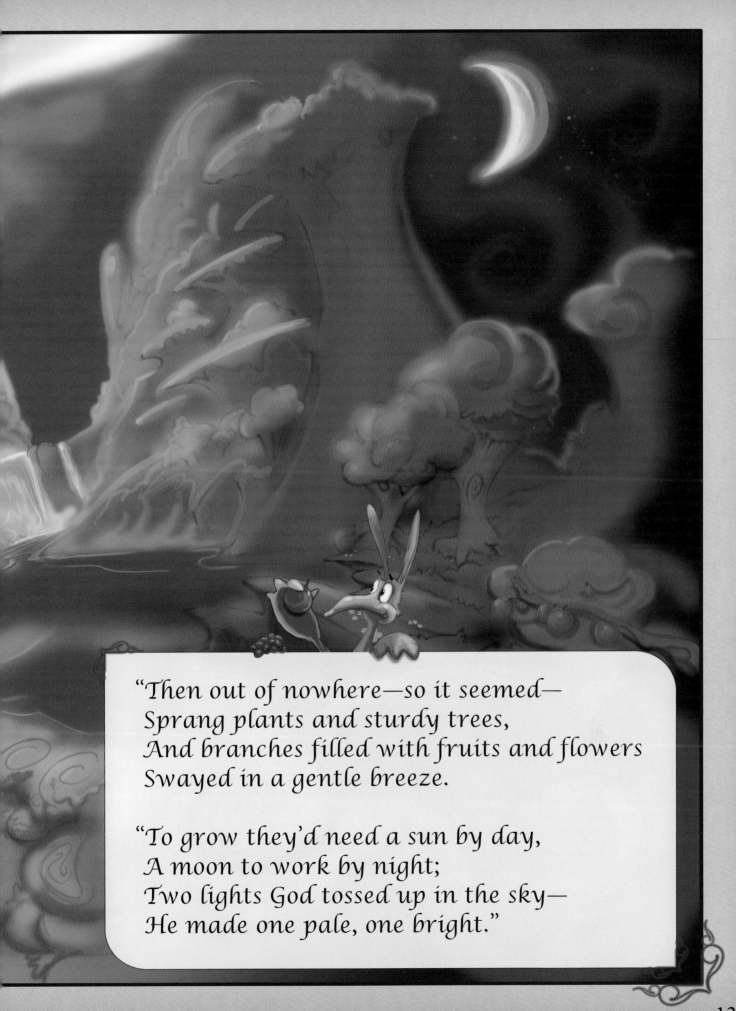

"Then out of nowhere—so it seemed—
Sprang plants and sturdy trees,
And branches filled with fruits and flowers
Swayed in a gentle breeze.

"To grow they'd need a sun by day,
A moon to work by night;
Two lights God tossed up in the sky—
He made one pale, one bright."

"And while He was about this task,
God flung stars left and right;
Much farther than your eye can see,
It was an awesome sight. [7]

"Wow! Just like magic, don't you think?"
I shook my head and said;
"No, not like magic; that's just tricks.
Try 'miracle' instead."

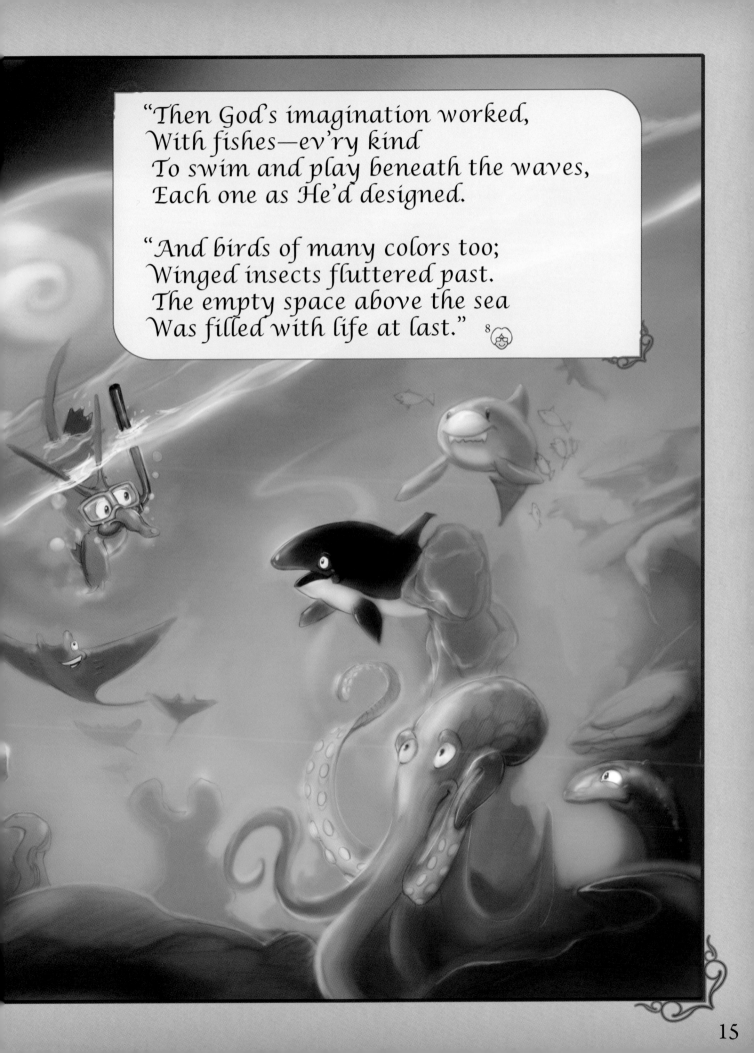

"Then God's imagination worked,
With fishes—ev'ry kind
To swim and play beneath the waves,
Each one as He'd designed.

"And birds of many colors too;
Winged insects fluttered past.
The empty space above the sea
Was filled with life at last." 8

15

"But still that was not quite enough,
On land from shore to shore;
God made a host of living things—
Apes, dinosaurs and more." [9]

"Now have you seen a tiny mouse,
Brown bear—opossum too?
And what about the elephants
That live in every zoo?" [10]

"Yes, all of these and many more,
God made in just one day;
And woolly sheep and kangaroos,
With great big lions would play." [11]

"Amazing though this was for sure,
We'd better not forget;
Remember God was waiting for
Someone He'd not made yet."

"So from the ground He took some clay,
And molded tenderly
A human form, and only one,
A man built perfectly." [12]

"Then slowly and with gentle breath,
God gave the man his life;
And after just a little while,
Brought to the man his wife."

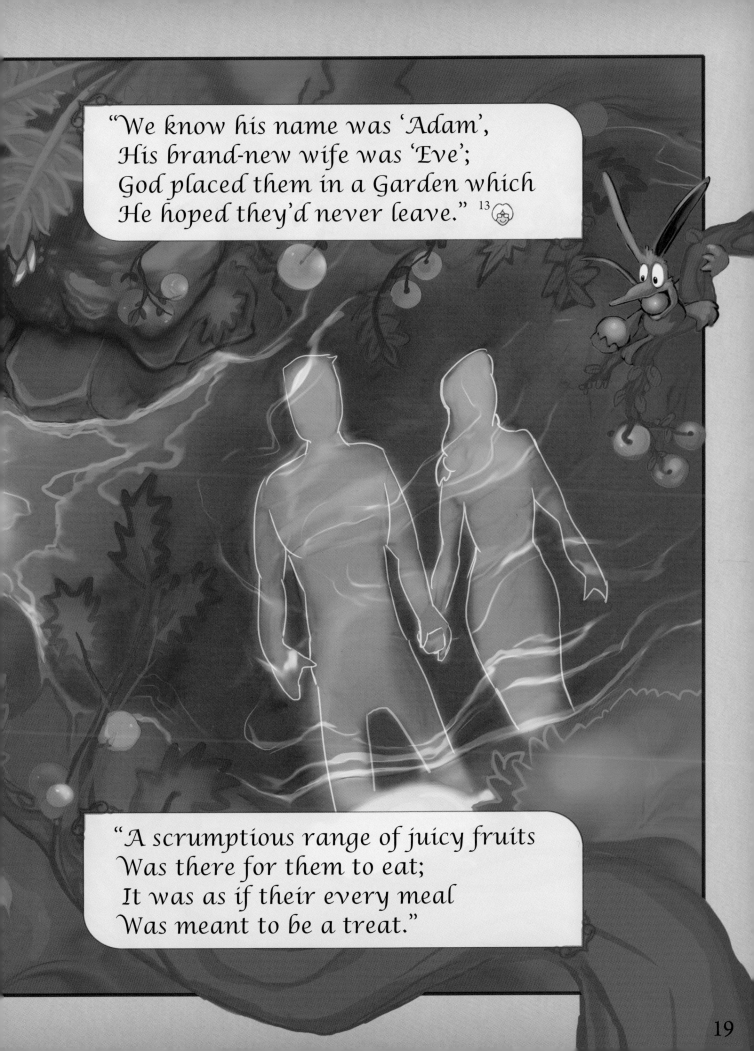

"We know his name was 'Adam',
His brand-new wife was 'Eve';
God placed them in a Garden which
He hoped they'd never leave." [13]

"A scrumptious range of juicy fruits
Was there for them to eat;
It was as if their every meal
Was meant to be a treat."

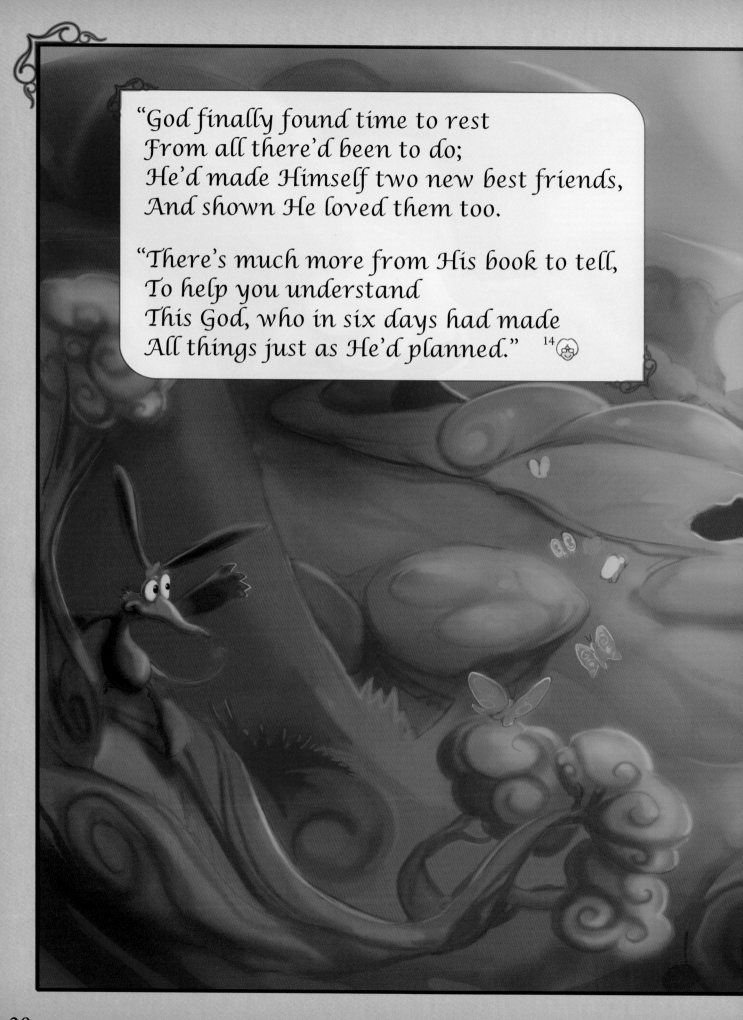

"God finally found time to rest
From all there'd been to do;
He'd made Himself two new best friends,
And shown He loved them too.

"There's much more from His book to tell,
To help you understand
This God, who in six days had made
All things just as He'd planned." [14]

"But that will have to wait, I guess,
Until another day;
Your mum will worry if she thinks
We went outside to play."

The two of us walked back inside
And quietly took our place.
We'd just spent special time alone;
I saw that in her face.

The pastor's message neared its end;
We'd both missed most of it.
Somehow I think that God above
Would not mind that one bit.

..: Nana Notes :..

[1] The little 'bilby' character is a native of Australia and a member of the bandicoot family of marsupials. The bilby is about the size of a rabbit. It lives mostly in dry areas of Australia, where it has become endangered, probably due to feral cats and foxes. A shy creature, it comes out at night when things are cooler; during the heat of the day it lives in one of several spiral burrows it has dug to escape things that want to eat it (it's a fallen world!). It sometimes eats other (smaller) furry animals, too, but mostly it eats insects, grubs, seeds, and fruit. Like other marsupials, it has a pouch to raise its young. But its pouch is designed to point backwards, not forwards like a kangaroo's, to avoid it getting filled up with dirt as the bilby burrows.

Bilby was chosen because of his big, hairless ears, which give him very acute hearing—and hearing is very important when someone is reading a story to a child. Not only for the child of course, but also for the reader. Children will ask the most convoluted questions, and we must listen very hard to not only what is being said but to what they actually *mean*, so that we can provide the answers they are genuinely seeking. The Bible says that faith comes by hearing, and hearing by the Word of God (Romans 10:17)—which includes proclaiming, expounding and explaining ('preaching') its truths.

A soft toy bilby has been to the Top of the World!! In May 1997, Tashi Tenzing—grandson of Tenzing Norgay, one of the two men who first conquered Mount Everest—reached the summit himself. The following extract is from a book written by Tashi and his wife Judy:

"On the very top of my pack I had attached a small, fluffy toy bilby, which is a highly endangered Australian marsupial. My son had asked me to carry it and it also symbolised my heartfelt wish to conserve the wild places and creatures of this amazing planet."

Tenzing Norgay and the Sherpas of Everest, by Judy and Tashi Tenzing 2001
More on bilbies: members.optusnet.com.au/bilbies/About_Bilbies.htm.

The endangered bilby.

Image source: Deparment of Evironment and Resource Management (QLD)

2 Because of their trust in a significant adult, few children in this age group will immediately wonder where Nana's knowledge comes from—the Bible, of course. The truth and authority of God's 'Book' (p. 20) are totally presupposed. Parents are encouraged to both provoke and respond to questions about 'how Nana knows this', as appropriate for their child's level of interest and comprehension. The selection of articles at creation.com/bible-questions-and-answers will help you answer deeper questions about the Bible from older children.

3   Most children will have experienced the fury of a thunderstorm—loud thunder, brilliant lightning and fierce wind. The storm must simply run its course. Humans cannot turn it on or turn it off. This 'mighty force' of God's power that moved at the creation of earth and universe, by the very nature of the work that was done, must have been countless times greater than any storm experienced on this planet. Greater than the biggest cyclone, tornado or hurricane we could ever imagine. But we need to remember that this was a controlled force. After a storm we see lots of damage, with trees, houses, cars, boats and planes scattered like toys. When the infinite-yet-personal moved as this 'mighty force' a beautiful planet and astonishing universe were created and nothing was destroyed. An excellent example of this controlling power is found in the story of Jesus calming the storm on the Sea of Galilee (Mark 4:35–41).

---

4   How to explain the inexplicable? All illustrations have limitations, so it might pay to use several. Here's just one: time is made up of past, present, and future (each is time, but the three things aren't each other and they are distinct while having the same 'essence'—they are all still 'time'). The Bible clearly defines the different roles of Father, Son and Holy Spirit, but there is never any change in characteristics or personality. These three 'persons' are one. From the Bible, we can understand that there is love (John 15:9) and communication (Genesis 1:26; 11:7) between the members of this 'tri-unity' (or trinity). See also John 1:1–14. For much more on this important subject, see: creation.com/god-questions-and-answers#trinity.

5 YHWH or יהוה in Hebrew—the most sacred name for God. YHWH is the God of Abraham and his descendants and is a personal name that means "I AM That I AM" (Exodus 3:14). For the Jewish people, this name for God became so sacred that they ceased to say it. There are other 'gods' in history given different names, and they make an interesting study—but there is only one YHWH, the One who made everything there is, and we find the truth about Him in the pages of the Bible.

6 Creation is ultimately all about relationships. The Father, Son and Holy Spirit have been in relationship with each other from eternity past (John 14:11, 3:35). So I would definitely avoid suggesting that God was 'lonely', but rather He decided to expand this relationship already in existence. To do that, the three-in-one God chose to design a world into which beings who resembled Him, at least in their spiritual aspects, could live forever. For a little child, 'forever' is of course a concept they can't really grasp—neither can we fully grasp it, come to think of it. But for them, a birthday a day away is 'forever' away. But they can understand arriving in a world that is ready and waiting for them—significant people who care for them and treasure them, air to breathe, water to drink, food to eat and a safe place to sleep. All of that was there 'before' ever they were, a lot of it put in place by loving and caring adults. And so it was with God and our first parents. Perhaps, as an adult, you might like to read "Did God create man to be an eternal companion for his son Jesus Christ?" (creation.com/companion)—I found this very helpful on this whole subject of man's relationship with God.

7 Space and what's in it interests most children, and by the time they are 5 or 6 they can have a simple understanding of at least our own solar system. This subject is normally covered to some extent even in the early years of education, and what child has not stood amazed on a starry, starry night and wondered at the array of lights stretched across the sky? The heavens really do declare the glory of God (Psalm 19:1), and this is a great time to talk about that. Maybe it was a little like blowing bubbles with a bubble pipe—but of course if we can think of God 'letting loose' the planets and stars (after creating them with just His Word—Psalm 33:9), He would have kept perfect control of them. Whereas with bubbles, we have no control over where they go and indeed we cannot stop them from exploding and disappearing in an instant.

8 All birds and water creatures were safe. Whatever they ate back then, it was certainly not each other, but originally plants were to be their only food (Genesis 1:30). Can you imagine jumping into a river and playing tag with a crocodile? Or having a huge pterodactyl as a pet? What a happy place it must have been—birds singing, fish jumping, with nothing more for them to do than eat, sleep and play. What happened to change this? You will have to read Book 2: *Please, Nana ... What is Death?* It was this question, 'What is death?', that started me writing in this way. A little bird died and sparked a discussion that required more thought on my part.

9   Yes, even dinosaurs. They did exist, along with some other quite exotic animals that are no longer present on this planet—they've died out, like so many other creatures are still doing today. God made it plain by personally inscribing on stone that everything in the universe was made in those six days of Creation Week (Exodus 20:11). And lions and lambs could play together, with the lambs in no fear of their lives. For everything you ever needed to know about dinosaurs, see: creation.com/dinosaur-questions-and-answers.

---

10   From biblical and biological considerations, we know that one 'kind' of animal may include several species. So today's lions and tigers, which can still interbreed to give ligers and tigons, are descended from the same biblical kind, as were many other cat species. Equally, sheep and goats were the same kind once. So 'lions and lambs' would not have looked exactly like the ones of today (not much of an issue given our 'cartoon-type' illustrations). This concept is mentioned here for parental guidance and consideration as to when to discuss it in an age-appropriate way. For further information, see creation.com/ligers.

---

11   See Genesis 1:30. Also, Isaiah 11:6 and 65:25, which refer to a future time of (at least partial—see Isaiah 65:20) restoration of Edenic conditions. They further affirm that there was no death of living creatures (*nephesh chayyah*, which does not include plants) in the pre-Fall world. For more, see chapter 6, "How did 'bad things' come about" in *The Creation Answers Book*, Creation Book Publishers, Powder Springs, GA 2009 (chapter available as a pdf at creation.com/cab6).

12 The Bible has two accounts of the creation story—in Genesis 1 and 2. See creation.com/genesis-questions-and-answers if people try to tell you about so-called 'contradictions' in Genesis. These chapters don't contradict each other; they each tell the story from a different perspective. For example, in chapter 2 we have a fuller account of the creation of the first man (Adam) from the dust of the ground and his wife (Eve) from one of Adam's ribs. See creation.com/rib for further fascinating information on how ribs today grow back!

13 Adam and Eve were to live in a garden—a very special place where they had a pleasant, sheltered life and where they could live happy and contented lives. They were instructed to tend the garden (Genesis 2:15) and to rule all of creation responsibly (Genesis 1:26). The same verse indicates that they were to have babies so as to fill the earth with their descendants (the meaning of the English word *replenish* has changed since the King James Bible was written; at the time it meant simply 'fill', not 'refill'). It would be an easy life filled with joy and happiness and totally without pain and suffering of any kind. That's why, when the Bible talks about everything being restored in the future (Acts 3:21), it is clear that it will be put back to a sinless, deathless condition (Revelation 21:4), because that is what it once was. And where exactly was this garden? Could we go to the place on Earth where it was? For the answer to this fascinating question see creation.com/eden (and it may not be what you expect, but I think you'll agree it makes great sense).

¹⁴  The Bible is very clear—God did all of this in six earth-rotation days, with an evening and a morning, and He rested on Day 7. By the way, creation.com/daysbeforesun will tell you how there could be evening and morning for the first three days before the sun was made,

For further material on this whole fascinating subject of creation, science and the Bible, see creation.com—and for more stories and things relevant for children, go to creation.com/creation-for-kids.

Also from Creation Book Publishers

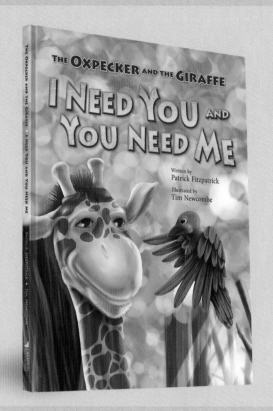

The Oxpecker and the Giraffe: I Need You and You Need Me

A delightful children's nature story told in 'Dr. Seuss-style' rhyme about an oxpecker bird who removes ticks and other nasties from the skin of a giraffe, for the benefit of both. With captivating artwork, it uses these two zany characters to teach about God's design, and about relationships, in a way that young children can easily understand and enjoy.

Days 1–7: Your complete children's guide to the 7 days of Creation Week

A full-color, glossy and beautifully illustrated guide to what God did on each day of Creation Week. It presents the truth about creation in a way that will stimulate young minds and answer questions such as: Who made God? Is there life on Mars? Could the days have been millions of years? What about the big bang? Did God use evolution? A compilation of articles that have appeared in the 'Creation for Kids' section of *Creation* magazine, it points children to Jesus Christ, the Creator and Savior God.